Rescue!

Grace Darling's Story

by Michael Sandler
illustrated by Nicole Tadgell

Harcourt
SCHOOL PUBLISHERS

Requests for permission to make copies of any part of the work should be addressed to School Permissions and Copyrights, Harcourt, Inc., 6277 Sea Harbor Drive, Orlando, Florida 32887–6777. Fax: 407-345-2418.

HARCOURT and the Harcourt Logo are trademarks of Harcourt, Inc., registered in the United States of America and/or other jurisdictions.

Printed in China

ISBN-10: 0-15-350548-6
ISBN-13: 978-0-15-350548-5

Ordering Options
ISBN-10: 0-15-350335-1 (Grade 5 Below-Level Collection)
ISBN-13: 978-0-15-350335-1 (Grade 5 Below-Level Collection)
ISBN-10: 0-15-357547-6 (package of 5)
ISBN-13: 978-0-15-357547-1 (package of 5)

11 12 13 14 15   0940   12 11 10

Nineteenth century sea captains didn't have radios. They didn't have radar. They relied on the beams of a lighthouse to warn them when they came close to shore.

The bright lighthouse lamps burned inflammable oils like kerosene. Lighthouse keepers kept these lamps lit at night. Often, keepers lived in the lighthouses with their families. Grace Darling grew up in an English lighthouse during the early nineteenth century. This is Grace's story.

I didn't expect to become a hero. I never thought I'd be famous. Why would I? Hardly anyone knew I was alive!

We lived on a tiny island surrounded by the sea. There were no other families on the island. It was just the four of us: Mum, Dad, and my younger brother, Willie. Four of us were living in a 75-foot (23 m) tall lighthouse.

When I was younger, the house had been full. One by one, however, my six older brothers and sisters had left. They went to live on the mainland. They went to find jobs, husbands, or wives.

We seldom had any visitors. Why would anyone come to this quiet, lonely place?

The nearby waters were very dangerous. Jagged rocks hid beneath the surface. They lay waiting to rip apart ships. Many had sunk here. People talked about ghosts that swam in the waves.

Life was quiet and simple. Keeping the lighthouse lamp burning was the most important task. My father conducted his work seriously. He knew how sea captains depended upon him.

The night that changed our quiet lives was one terrible September evening. A storm was blowing in. The winds were awful. They howled and whistled around the tall walls of the lighthouse. A little after midnight, my father asked me to help him outside.

"Come, Grace," he said. "This night is going to be nasty."

Steadying myself against the wind, I followed him. We tied up our rowboat. We moved things inside. In a storm like this, anything loose would be blown away.

Then we returned into the safety of the lighthouse. Mum and Dad went to bed. I couldn't sleep at all. The storm was too wild and loud.

At around 5:00 A.M., I went up to the top of the lighthouse. Staring out into the sea, I saw something. Out by the Big Harcar Rocks was a huge, dark shape.

I ran downstairs and woke father. He came up to look. With the first rays of the sun, the dark shape became clearer. It was a ship, a big one! It looked like a paddlewheel steamer. The storm had driven it into the rocks. It was shattered, nearly torn in two! Had anyone survived?

At first, it was hard to tell. The skies were still gray. The rain was still coming down heavily. Using a telescope, however, we finally saw them. Out on the rock, inches above the waves, people were crawling around.

In this storm, no rescuers could make it from the mainland. The surviving passengers had only one hope: us.

"Father," I said. "We must help them. They won't last long!"

At first, my father said nothing. His look was deadly serious. He was deep in thought. I knew what he was thinking about—the rowboat.

The boat was about twenty feet (6 m) long. Normally, it took three or four rowers to handle such a large boat. In calm water, two people could manage it. Now, however, the sea wasn't calm. It was furious.

My younger brother was on the mainland. There were only the two of us to row. To rescue the passengers, we would have to do it ourselves.

"Let's try, Grace," said my father, breaking his silence. "If we don't, they will surely die."

While climbing into the rowboat, I looked back at our lighthouse. Would I ever see it again? My mother watched us leave. I could see the fear in her eyes.

We pushed off into the waves as the wind drove rain into our eyes. The waves shoved our tiny boat this way and that. Several times we nearly broached. All we could do was pull hard at the oars.

I rowed and rowed and rowed. I tried to keep fear from my mind. I tried not to think about the boat tipping over. I tried to ignore the pain in my arms.

We kept moving forward. Somehow, we made it to the Big Harcar Rocks. The nine survivors of the shipwreck huddled on the slippery stone. They looked cold and miserable, yet when they saw us, their faces changed. Suddenly, they were full of hope.

As they scrambled toward us, my father jumped onto the rock. He held up his hands to stop them.

"This boat is small. We can't take you all in one trip," he yelled. He was screaming. The wind was so loud that they wouldn't have heard him otherwise. "Just five now. We'll come back for the rest of you."

I tried to steady the boat as five of them climbed aboard. Their weight pushed us down into the water. For a second, I thought we would sink. Then my father turned the boat back toward our island. It was easier than before. Three of the passengers helped out with the oars. I slumped back to rest. I don't think I could have paddled one more stroke.

I helped three of the passengers out once we
reached shore. My father and the others headed
back to pick up those who were left behind.

I led the survivors into the lighthouse. They
were shivering, half-drowned after their night on
the rock. My mother sat them in front of the fire
and covered them with blankets.

A while later, my father returned with the
others. We tried to warm them up as well.

I was so proud of what we'd done. Still,
I didn't suspect what would happen as a result.
News got out about the rescue. Our quiet island
became much busier.

At first, it was just a few. Then more and more people arrived. Boat after boat pulled up at the dock. There were rowdy reporters. They were noisy and full of questions. They didn't want to talk to father. They wanted to talk to me!

They seemed surprised. How could a young girl do such a thing? How could she row through a wicked storm?

I guess it was unusual. Rowing was a part of island life for me. Girls from other places, however, usually didn't row.

Every day, I answered questions. I sat and posed while artists painted my picture. Visitors kept coming.

My poor Mum! She spent all of her time keeping the house clean. She was always worried. A dignified visitor might arrive and find the house in a mess.

My father grumbled that the island was now too busy. "I almost wish I'd never rescued them," he'd say.

I knew he was joking. He felt the same as I did. If you have the chance to save a life, you must, even if it changes your own.

Think Critically

1. Describe Grace's life before the rescue. How was it different afterwards?

2. Why are lighthouses probably less important today than they were in the nineteenth century?

3. Why do you think people were so interested in Grace's story?

4. If you were Grace's father, would you have gone ahead with the rescue? Why or why not?

5. What did you learn from this story?

 **Social Studies**

Before and After Find out more about the nineteenth century. Write a paragraph about how life was different then from now. Write a second paragraph about how life may have been the same.

School-Home Connection Tell a family member about the story and the decision Grace's father made. Ask that person if he or she would have made the same choice and why. Then share what you would have done.

Word Count: 1,189